CHINESE CERAMICS
IN THE
ASHMOLEAN MUSEUM

An illustrated handbook to the collections

By
MARY TREGEAR

ASHMOLEAN MUSEUM OXFORD

1987

First published 1979 (ISBN 0 9000 9058 8). Second edition, containing a glossary of the revised romanisation of Chinese terms, published 1987.

ISBN 0 907849 57 1

ASHMOLEAN MUSEUM PUBLICATIONS

Middle Eastern and Far Eastern art and archaeology
Treasures of the Ashmolean
Eastern Ceramics from the collection
of Gerald Reitlinger
Medieval Middle Eastern Pottery
Medieval Syrian Pottery
The Ancient Near East
The Indian Collections
Chinese Greenware
Oriental Lacquer

British Library Cataloguing in Publication Data

Ashmolean Museum
Chinese ceramics in the Ashmolean
Museum. – 2nd ed.
1. Porcelain, Chinese   2. Pottery, Chinese
I. Title   II. Tregear, Mary
738'.0951   NK4165

ISBN 0-907849-57-1

Cover design by Roy Cole

Reprinted in Great Britain from the original film, set in Times series 327, by Cheney and Sons Ltd., Banbury, Oxon. 1987

Contents

Notes for the Reader

1. The numbers which appear in brackets in the plate captions are the serial numbers of the objects in the accessions registers of the Department of Eastern Art.

2. Measurements are given in both centimetres and inches. Ht.=height   D.=diameter

3. The romanisation of Chinese terms on the labels in the Chinese display have been changed from the Wade-Giles system to Pin yin. This is to conform to the now officially accepted system in China. A glossary of this change is provided giving a cross-reference for use with this handbook, in which the romanisation is in the Wade-Giles system. Where the spelling is the same in both systems the term has not been included in the list.

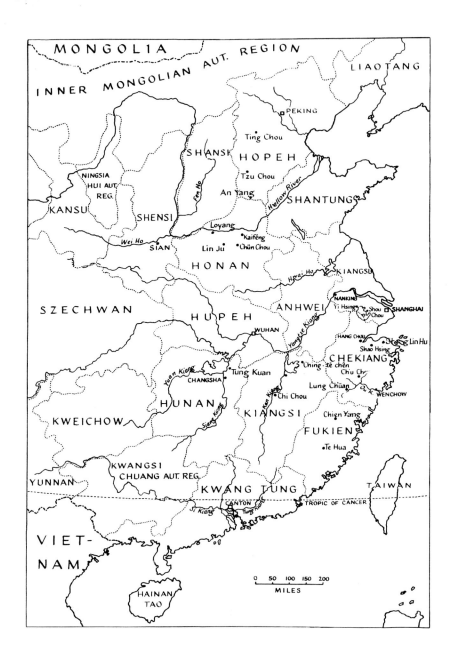

Introduction

This handbook is intended as a concise guide to the Ashmolean collections of Chinese ceramics. The museum galleries show notable examples of most of the major types of Chinese pottery. Just as this display is not an exhaustive coverage of the subject so the guide is not a comprehensive survey of the history of the potter's craft in China, but is an attempt to explain further the examples to be seen, and as such proceeds in a chronological sequence.

Beautiful as these pieces are in their own right and readily appreciated by everyone, they are also adjuncts to a complex, sophisticated culture in which the connoisseur was sensitive to all forms of artistic expression. Amongst the many crafts of China, pottery has often held a special place which changed as the structure of society evolved with the culture. Painting and calligraphy, early the major art, were accepted as the chief expressive art of the scholar gentleman. Indeed painting overtook calligraphy and was refined to become an ascetic art form practised by the same scholar gentleman under restrictions of material and format which resulted in characteristic monochrome compositions in a highly idiosyncratic style. It seems that with the refinement and restriction of painting in China the applied arts, with which the connoisseur surrounded himself, took on a special status. The scholar gentleman became a most discerning collector. This can explain to some degree the love of pottery, the appreciation of the form, the colour and the texture of the glaze and later of decoration, all qualities understressed or missing from his painting. The scholar painter of say the later Sung period was not as limited in his artistic appreciation as his landscape and bamboo painting might lead one to believe for he also treasured his Ting ware and celadon, his black glazed wares and lavender Chün, (Fig. 13, 14 & 16). These took their place with the antique bronzes, the carved ink stone and jade and the carefully contrived garden which enriched his surroundings and to which his elegant ink painting added a very special aesthetic flavour, part visual part philosophical.

The potters, always anonymous and working as a craft guild, achieved many beautiful styles and techniques. In the technical field the Chinese potters have so often been the innovators that the very name of the country is applied to a class of fine porcelain. Style and technique developed hand in hand and were as often influenced by the patron as by the market. In a culture where traditions persist this aspect adds an extra dimension, for the patron very soon became an antique collector or a collector of archaism. Thus the 18th century admiration for the Sung taste encouraged the many archaisms of the Ching-te-chen kilns. Even more than this, the changing status of material becomes evident. Where the original was a practical and ubiquitous pot, with the passage of time and more particularly with the advent of trade, that same pot has now acquired a new valuation often of little relevance to its original one. There are several considerations in the total appreciation of Chinese ceramics which can enrich their interest for the viewer, and it is hoped that some at least of these can be found in the gallery display.

Neolithic – Bronze Age

From Shantung and Anhwei in the east to Kansu in the west, the people in the widespread Neolithic settlements of north China all made pottery of a range of styles. This included a coarse cord-impressed ware, for daily use, very low-fired with a gritty coarse body; but the most distinctive pottery was a burnished ware, fired either red or black. The red bodied wares were characteristically decorated with black, white and red slip designs which probably were distinctive to each locality. Some of the more strikingly decorated wares come from the Kansu, central Yellow River basin and its tributary the Wei river (Fig. 1). Further east a sophisticated and

Fig. 1. Urn, red and black slip decorated unglazed red earthenware. Neolithic, 'Painted Pottery'. *c.* 2500 BC.
Ht.13″ 33.0 cms. [1956.847] Ingram Gift.

1

elegantly turned black ware was produced. All the higher quality Wares are made of the loessic earth common to the Yellow river basin, a fine grained material which was low fired and was made by coil and hand moulding. The body is of even thickness and the mouth is often not a true circle which all seems to indicate that a wheel was not yet in common use although a turn-table was already a well known tool. The firing was done in very simple up-draught kilns, a pit holding the fire with a perforated cover. The more elaborately produced pots are found in burials clustered around the body and although they had been assumed to have been made specifically for burial rites it is now considered, partly because of the sheer quantity found, that they may well have been used by the living prior to burial.

Shang and Chou dynasties

With the introduction of bronze and bronze-casting, pottery seems to have lost much of its special status, although potters continued to make utilitarian cord impressed wares. In China metal craft was dependent on moulds and casting therefore relied on ceramic craftsmanship. Thus, the development of technical skills during the bronze age, even though pottery was not of a very high status, can be understood in terms of the craftsmen moving between the two crafts and consequently learning the handling properties and firing characteristics of clay. The potters of the eastern areas gradually evolved a higher fired ware using their indigenous feldspathic clays and probably a more sophisticated down draught kiln. The gradual development of stoneware over many centuries introduced a whole new role for pottery. It was possible then to make a water tight vessel which was very strong. The plasticity of the local clay and the potter's wheel now in universal use, also allowed the potter to make a variety of simple and beautiful shapes. In the Chou period much effort went into the creation of replicas of the revered bronze vessels. (Fig. 2)

Of particular interest at this period of the 4th-3rd century BC is the potting done in the Shao Hsing area of north Chekiang. This was to prove a long lasting tradition of high-fired potting over the next 14 hundred years, along the few hundred miles from Shao Hsing eastward to Shang lin Hu. The clay here was plastic, ferruginous and

2

Fig. 2. *Ho* replica of a bronze, grey earthenware with traces of yellowish glaze. *c.* 4th-3rd century BC.
Ht.7½″ 19.05 cms. [1956.929] Ingram Gift.

developed its own glaze readily with the addition of an ash flux. The mastery of the wheel and high firing kilns in the area led to a tradition of stoneware which was the basis for the very beautiful Sung celadons of central southern Chekiang. The method of firing ensured a

3

reducing atmosphere and so the ferruginous clay and glaze produced a grey body and blue-green glaze which was gradually refined. The earliest examples are replicas of bronzes but the potters soon developed a vocabulary of shapes specific to the throwing techniques of the wheel. (Fig. 3).

Fig. 3. Covered jar, grey stoneware with a green glaze. Chekiang ware. 4th century AD.
Ht.8¼" 20.95 cms. [1956.947] Ingram Gift.

Han dynasty

Contemporary with this gradually developing stoneware tradition centred in Chekiang, and also probably in Shensi, was a different tradition in the making of low-fired ware. This was used for tiles and stamped bricks, for crocks and all sorts of utility wares but also for the burial furniture which has been preserved in some quantity. This last class of potting saw the development of a glazed low-fired ware using a lead fluxed glaze. This glaze appears to have been an introduced technique, possibly from the Near East, for the Han dynasty was a period of lively contact with the techniques and materials of central Asia and the western asiatic people. In China, where earthenware was already well understood, the addition of a glaze using a lead flux produced an acidic glaze in which the copper colouring agent developed a deep green. Low firing always took place in an oxidising atmosphere and the possibilities of brighter colours, using metallic oxide colouring agents, slowly emerged. The Han potters of the metropolitan area of the central Yellow River region made a wide variety of lead glazed wares, all green in colour but ranging in shapes from replicas of bronze vessels to models of animals and houses (Fig. 4). These were made for burial to conform to contemporary ideas of the after life as a version of earthly life requiring all its comforts and accoutrements. As the distribution of wealth changed and families could no longer afford to bury treasures and bronzes or indeed even everyday objects with their dead, a tradition of model making specially for this purpose was established. The earliest of these seem to have been the life size clay models found at the site of the Ch'in emperor's tomb near Sian, but immediately taken up, in miniature, by the aristocratic society of Lo Yang and Ch'ang An. The northern green glaze reacts to burial in the same way as its mediterranean counterpart, the moisture and salts attack the glaze, layering it to produce a mother of pearl irridescence. The animals and human figurines were either modelled from the solid clay or made in moulds, joined at a centreline. The casual execution of these burial wares points to their ephemeral nature, they were made simply for funerary rites and produced inexpensively. In South China similar tomb furniture was made but without glaze and in a slightly higher fired ware which sometimes developed a

Fig. 4. Tomb model of a house, unglazed grey earthenware. Han dynasty from Canton.
$11\frac{3}{4}'' \times 11\frac{1}{4}''$ 29.8 cms. × 28.5 cms. [1969.51] Gift of Mrs. K. Schofield in memory of Walter Schofield.

brownish sheen, not a true glaze but a fusion of the surface of the body.

By contrast the hard high fired wares of the Han period, (Fig. 5) although not fully investigated, include a group of heavy storage jars. These are of a true stoneware with a thick and dense grey body; the shoulder and neck or lip have often developed a green/brown glaze which appears in many cases to be a fortuitous production as the surface of the stoneware body fuses. However, it soon became a true glaze, a lime fluxed alumina silica glaze probably made by the addition of slaked lime to body clay. The colour would be due to the iron present in the body clay. The kiln or kilns making these jars

6

Fig. 5. *Hu* shaped jar. Grey stoneware with incised decoration and greenish glaze on shoulder. Han dynasty.
Ht. 14¼″ 26.19 cms. [1956.926] Ingram Gift.

7

have not been identified and they have been found over too wide an area of Honan, Kiangsi and Chekiang to make even an informed guess as to the general location whence they came. Apparently the potters were exploring the possibilities of their materials and although the bronze derivation of their shapes is still visible, simple wheel thrown shapes gradually dominate and decoration is stamped or incised while the pot is on the wheel. The glaze is now quite deliberately applied and the long process of refinement of a reduced-iron coloured glaze to produce a blue green over an ever paler grey body is undertaken. The earliest identifiable kiln area for this greenware is at Chiu Yen associated with the market at Shao Hsing. The pots are typically of simple shapes, bowls, wide shouldered jars and basins, with complex impressed and appliqué decoration under the glaze. The distinctive many spurred kiln support leaves its scar either in the glaze on the base of three legged dishes or in the form of red haloed spur marks on the unglazed base of bowls and jars. Already, by the 3rd-4th century, the formation of foot rims was diverse and although there is no reason to suppose a widespread kiln area, the variety of wares remaining, mainly found in the Nanking, Wu or early Western Chin tomb excavations, seems to indicate a flourishing production. The body of this ware is rich in alumina silicate and fired at an estimated 1200°C-1300°C; it is a very strong stoneware. The glaze, which like the body is highly ferruginous, is a blue green colour on reduction firing; it is also an alumina silicate with an alkali-lime flux and fuses with the body. Typically, the flawing of these early pieces has been in the firing when kiln dirt has fallen on to the wet glaze. Alongside these richly decorated every-day wares are the tomb models and urns on which all clay modellers' techniques of impressing, appliqué, roulleting and incised line are used producing lively pieces all made of high fired green glazed stoneware. (Fig. 3)

This area of Chekiang was not firmly under Chinese administrative control and so the pots had a certain 'foreign' exoticism and they soon became collectors' items. Already at this period similarly hard and glazed wares were produced in Shensi the other great centre of high fired pottery production and so this respect can be well understood. It led to a long tradition of imitations of the green glazed grey stoneware by other notable kilns in north, south and west in later centuries.

Fig. 6. Large grey stoneware jar with appliqué decoration and dark green glaze (foot missing). Ching Hsien, Hopei. Nan Pei Ch'ao. Ht. $15\frac{1}{8}''$ 28.4 cms. [1956.964] Ingram Gift.

Chin and Nan Pei Ch'ao dynasties

Indeed, during the disturbed Chin and Nan Pei Ch'ao periods, when the country was divided, minor courts flourished and the movement of treasured objects probably became difficult. So that whilst the Shao Hsing kilns flourished and supplied a wide selection of richly decorated wares to the Wu State and its capital at Nanking, the northern Honan potters and the Shensi potters produced green glazed stoneware (Fig. 6) and white bodied wares for the Northern Wei court first at Ta T'ung and then at Lo Yang. The white Honan ware was initially not so high fired and consequently not so hard as the grey southern ware. But it is perhaps the successor to a tradition based on the rare white ware of Shang made at Anyang. The clay in the area of Honan – probably in the general region of Ting Chou – from which these wares derive is very fine grained alumina silicate and contains very little iron; the firing is traditionally assumed to be coal and resulted in a totally reduced firing. The effect of this is to produce a cool white/grey ware hard bodied with a characteristic smooth feel. There is no hint of oxidisation and no sign of kiln support except occasionally for a few traces of grit. The strong jars and bowls produced have a thin almost colourless transparent glaze which may vary from bluish to ivory. This white ware, presumably first made as a practical everyday pottery, was slowly refined, to produce a translucent white ware, porcelain, in the 6th century.

While these two great traditions of high fired wares, white in the north and grey green in the south developed, not totally unaware of each other but quite remote geographically, the production of low fired wares seems to have died down probably due to the dispersal of power and more modest burial customs.

Sui and T'ang dynasties

This situation changed with the re-unification of the country at first under the Sui dynasty and to a state of some magnificence under the T'ang dynasty. Great capitals were re-established at Lo Yang and Ch'ang An and metropolitan life became cosmopolitan and rich. Burial customs were elaborated and many models required. This time the potters produced mould made figures and replicas (Fig. 7),

10

Fig. 7. Tomb model of a camel, unglazed pale earthenware. T'ang dynasty. Ht. 11⅞" 28.0 cms. [1956.988] Ingram Gift.

again low fired but made of a white fine grained clay which occasionally burned pinkish in the oxidising firing and which also

Fig. 8. Tomb figure of a soldier guard. T'ang dynasty.
Ht. 18″ 46.00 cms. [×1258] Sayce Bequest.

developed rich metallic oxide colours in lead fluxed glaze. Probably again borrowing from the Middle Eastern potters, the Chinese began to use not only iron and copper in glaze but also cobalt. Thus they had a wide and bright palette from yellow to dark brown, green and blue. These were all put into the wet glaze which has a tendency to run as it melts on heating, virtue was made of this in the 'splashed' three colour ware of the 8th century. Otherwise the glazes were controlled by the use of raised cloisons or incised lines between the

Fig. 9. Three legged dish, white earthenware, incised decoration with three coloured glazes. T'ang dynasty.
D. 7½" 19.05 cms. [1956.1099] Ingram Gift.

colours (Fig. 9). The showy effect of these pieces was a great attraction as the grand families vied with each other to amass a rich assortment of furnishing for the family tombs and paraded their collections in the streets before burial. They are an echo of much richness of invention and decoration in more precious material surrounding these same families in life. The early T'ang period, and the 8th century in particular, was one of wealth in the new great cities which were being built. Exotic materials, glass and gold and silver, jade and inlaid bronze filled the homes of the gentry and the pottery which held its place with these was the quiet white ware from

Fig. 10. Covered jar, white earthenware from Hopei. T'ang dynasty.
Ht. 6″ 15.24 cms. [1956.1370] Ingram Gift.

the north and the equally sober green from Chekiang. The white
wares being delicate and sometimes translucent were inspired by

14

silver wares and glass and their Sasanian prototypes in ancient Persia (Fig. 10). The northern potters, characteristically flamboyant and adventurous in design and decoration produced elaborately decorated wares, white, and occasionally green glazed which show striking Mediterranean affinities in their motifs.

The southern potters, refining yet further their green glazed wares, had dropped all but the slightest surface decoration but enlarged their vocabulary of shapes and perfected a beautiful blue-green glaze (Fig. 11). The tradition was carried through to perhaps the first of the great connoisseurs' wares in the 10th century when the potters of Shang Lin Hu in north east Chekiang produced many qualities of green wares, the chief of which was known as Yüeh ware. This name comes from the old name of the area, the state of Yüeh, which was even yet not part of China although the ruler paid tribute to the Chinese court. The beautiful grey green ware played a valued part of that tribute, and became a part of the cult of tea drinking, a growing fashion in the 9th and 10th centuries. The 'Tea Classic', by Lu Yü (mid eighth century), lists the major potteries of the period in order of preference as tea bowls. The green wares of Chekiang are put at the head of the list. Poets writing of the beauty of their environment begin to mention pottery and particularly the quality of shape and glaze.

Lu Kuei-meng, a ninth century poet writing of Yüeh wares:

"When the Yüeh ware kilns are opened in the misty late autumn
The green colours of the thousand peaks are gathered in the bowls"

Hsü Yin, a T'ang poet writing verses to accompany a tribute gift of tea cups to the emperor:

"Like bright moons cunningly carved and dyed with spring water,
Like curling discs of thinnest ice, filled with green clouds,
Like ancient moss-eaten bronze mirrors lying upon a mat,
Like tender lotus leaves full of dew drops floating on the riverside"

The emperor Shih Tsung (954-9) writing his requirements to the potters frames them in a similar poetic vein:

"The blue of the sky after rain when the clouds have broken, this is exactly the colour which you must give to the porcelain".

15

Fig. 11. Spouted ewer, grey stoneware with green glaze. From Shang-lin
Hu, Chekiang. 10th century.
Ht. $7\frac{7}{8}''$ 19.95 cms. [1956.215] Ingram Gift.

Fig. 12. Spouted ewer, grey stoneware with appliqué cartouches, pale green glaze and dark brown splashes. From Changsha, Wa Chia P'ing, Hunan. Late T'ang dynasty.
Ht. 9″ 22.7 cms. [1973.8]

These are brief reminders of the position of the higher quality wares in the life of the educated aesthete, a class of ever increasing importance in Chinese society. They did not of course monopolise the market and the majority of Chinese pottery needs were met from local kilns producing quantities of hard wearing useful pots. Often these were in the general style of the 'high class' wares but they do bear the character of the local style particularly in the individual kiln stilting methods, the foot formation and decoration. So the Changsha potters made green glazed wares of distinction using their own lighter body material and appliqué and iron splash decoration (Fig. 12). The foot of bowls and jars alike are also distinctive and are used also on the white wares from these kilns .the Changsha and Tung Kuan kilns made both green and white as did also the early kilns at Ching-te-chen, Kiangsi.

Sung dynasty

The major wares of the highly sophisticated Northern Sung period (11th-12th century) centred around the northern kilns supplying the court at Kaifeng. The white wares from Ting Chou attracted the admiration of the connoisseurs. This lovely white bodied ware with an ivory translucent glaze is a special refinement of the earlier northern white ware. It was very thinly potted with a tiny foot, or no foot at all, on the bowls and dishes but, being fired on the rim in a seggar (Fig. 13), the rim is unglazed and is protected by a thin metal band clipped on after firing. The shapes of these pots seem still to reflect the silver wares probably current in China though earlier imported from the near east. The simply drawn floral decorations under the glaze started a tradition later transmitted to the south, as was also the more elaborate moulded decoration. This apparent duality of taste, for the simply elegant or the florid and elaborate, is one which is always present in China, it reflects both the size of the country and the complexity of society in which there was a diversity between the cultured scholar and the merchant, military and landlord groups. These groups often overlap and taste is rarely clear-cut but at any one period the arts and crafts and painting all echo a breadth of taste. So it is that in this period of 11th-12th century, even amongst the literati arbiters of taste, there was room for an admiration of

18

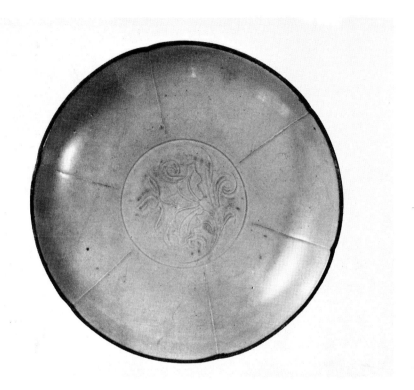

Fig. 13. Foliated dish, white stoneware with ivory glaze, incised decoration and metal rim. Ting ware Hopei. Sung dynasty.
D. 8″ 20.32 cms. [1956.1433] Ingram Gift.

both the delicacy of high class Ting ware and the sombre heavy restraint of Ju ware.

This is an exceptionally fine grey bodied green glazed ware made in the Lin Ju area of Shensi which acquired a high reputation as a 'Kuan' or official ware. It is today rare having been a connoisseurs' ware from the time of its production, and is better known by the imitations made in the south in the Hangchow area kilns and in the Lung Ch'uan products where it is called 'Kuan' ware. More widely known is the ware made at Chün Chou near to Kaifeng (Fig. 14); it is a very heavy strong ware of a buff tone which oxidises to a deep

Fig. 14. Food bowl, buff stoneware with blue glaze and purple splash (gold repair). Chün, Honan. Sung dynasty. D. 6⅞" 17.3 cms. [1965.523] Ingram Gift.

reddish brown and is slightly rough in texture. The many useful bowl, basin and jar shapes are covered, to the foot, in a thick hard glaze which is typically opaque pale lavender blue decorated by a purple splash. This is achieved by iron in the glaze with impurities and a tiny amount of copper put in to the raw glaze to produce the purple colour. These practical wares are every-day pots which gained some note and were copied in the South. The other large group of northern every-day wares is that called Tzu Chou (Fig. 15). This is an extensive and varied group characterised by a grey stoneware body, covered in a cream or dark brown slip over which is a colourless slightly milky hard glaze. The very distinctive decoration, bold bird and flower motifs painted in slip or incised through it, are common to all

Fig. 15. Deep bowl, grey stoneware decorated with cream and brown slip and colourless glaze. T'zu Chou, Hopei. Sung dynasty. Ht. $4\frac{7}{8}''$ 12.26 cms. [1956.1304].

the many Tzu Chou wares. The shapes again show its homely use, bowls, jars, pillows and dishes are common. All are sturdily made with a heavy everted foot ring and spur marks in the bowls where they have been stacked in the kiln. This ware is also imitated in the South. The move towards this imitation was accentuated by conquest of the northern part of the country by the Chin turkic peoples. These invading peoples themselves drove out the Mongols who had been troubling the Chinese from the north and they set up their own dynasty in north China, forcing the Chinese court to move to the Southern Sung capital in Hangchow. This move was influential in

21

many ways but very simply in terms of the potters, who were peasant people tied to their craft centres, it had the general effect of enlarging the access to central Asian objects for the northern craftsmen and of enlarging the patronage quite extraordinarily for the southern craftsmen. They now found themselves in the position of being required to satisfy the needs of a court and of the refugee metropolitan

Fig. 16. Food bowl, pale grey stoneware with crackled green glaze (Celadon) Lung Ch'üan, Chekiang. Southern Sung dynasty. D. 5¾" 14.6 cms. [1956.451] Ingram Gift.
'Celadon' is a European term denoting the distinctive grey-blue-green of Sung Lung Ch'üan wares. It is traditionally believed to have come from the name of Celadon, a shepherd in a 17th century romance 'L'Astrée' by Honore d'Urfé, who wore a grey-green dress. The name now denotes any grey-green stoneware. It is never used by oriental authorities.

people who settled in Hangchow. Not unnaturally the Chekiang and Kiangsi kilns were required to produce wares to either imitate or take the place of the favoured wares of Shensi and Honan. So it was that the celadon of central Chekiang, Lung Ch'üan, was raised in status in both China and Japan to become collectors' treasure. (Fig. 16). This pale grey bodied ware is heavier than the Shang Lin Hu

22

ware of north Chekiang but has a beautiful bluish green glaze which at its finest is thick and suffused with tiny bubbles, a feature of many Sung glazes. The thickness of the glaze masks any precision of potting but the shapes produced at this kiln area in central south Chekiang are in classic shapes, bowls, tripods, jars and dishes mostly undecorated although incised motifs are not unknown and a favourite was the lotus petal relief on the outside of a bowl. The foot rim of the

Fig. 17. Spittoon, grey stoneware with grey green glaze (Kuan type), Lung Ch'üan, Chekiang. Southern Sung dynasty. D. 5$\frac{3}{16}$" 13.0 cms. [1956.1352] Ingram Gift.

Lung Ch'üan bowl or jar is usually unglazed, the body being oxidised red. The glaze comes right down to the foot outside and is cursorily applied inside on the cut out base. The tell tale of the southern body and firing technique is the little rim of red at the edge of the glaze. The Lung Ch'uan potters, having established a major kiln area, also made 'Kuan' wares which are distinguishable by their shapes (Fig. 17).

23

The south eastern province of Fukien was becoming a notable ceramic area by the 13th century. The local potters of Chien Yang made a very dark bodied stoneware which they glazed with an impure

Fig. 18. Tea bowl, dark brown stoneware, dark streaked Temmoku glaze (Hare's fur). Chien yang Fukien. Southern Sung. D. 2½″ 6.3 cms. [1956.767] Ingram Gift.

ferruginous mixture giving a distinctive 'hares fur' streaky dark glaze (Fig. 18). The products of this kiln included all the usual everyday shapes but understandably predominantly bowls of various sizes as these are the vessels most used in China. The growing and drinking of tea was a cult adopted by the Ch'an (Zen) Buddhist sect which was establishing big temples in Chekiang at this time and the dark tea bowls were adopted, with the green wares of Lung Ch'uan, as peculiar

24

to the ceremony. The Japanese Buddhists visited China at this time to learn the practices of the Ch'an sect and went to the temple near Tien Mu Shan outside Hangchow. There they found the Fukien bowls being used and must have assumed that they came from the region because they gave the ware the name Temmoku, (the Japanese reading of Tien Mu Shan), and took them back to Japan where they were revered and imitated and inspired the Raku potters. Temmoku

Fig. 19. Tea bowl, buff stoneware with mottled brown/cream glazes (Temmoku) Chi Chow, Kiangsi. Southern Sung. D. 3¾" 9.5 cms. [×1266] Sayce Bequest.

ware as it is now popularly known was copied by many kilns notably the Kiangsi kilns at Chi Chow where the glazing is spectacular but the potting of the buff body cursory (Fig. 19). The Honan potters also made their version but, within their own traditions of dark glazing, on an elegantly potted pale body. The last but greatest major kiln of the

25

Sung period is at Ching-te-chen in Kiangsi. This complex on the Yangtse flood plain had been in production since the T'ang dynasty and is still a major porcelain factory area today. During the Sung dynasty it first came into prominence as the source of high quality white porcelain in the South. The southern version of the creamy

Fig. 20. Foliated deep bowl, porcelain with Ying Ch'ing glaze (repaired) Ching-te-chen, Kiangsi. Sung dynasty.
D. 6¼" 15.87 cms. [×1157] Sayce Bequest.

coloured Ting ware is a pale blue white ware which is translucent and is called Ying Ch'ing as descriptive of the faintly blue colour (Fig. 20). The sources of clays for the Ching-te-chen potters were close at hand in the volcanic granite in w'-ich the intrusion of fine grained mica compounds produce a natu .l flux. This ample supply of raw material and easy access by water (by canal and river) to the main cities, must have encouraged the growth of a community of specialised

26

skills which led to the choice of Ching-te-chen as the centre for an Imperial office and the source of court wares from the 15th century. The fine Ying Ch'ing porcelain formed the basis for the many decorated wares produced from the Yüan period to the present day. Sung Ying Ch'ing wares are of true porcelain being translucent, the forms are of the traditional southern types. The silver and glass forms of the northern Ting wares were taken up, even to the extent of a production of bowls fired on the rim. This last technique was not practised for long. The tendency was to develop a tall foot and, as the custom grew for the combining of bowls with stands and covers, not always of the same material, an exaggeration of proportion until a stemmed cup appeared toward the end of the period. The delicacy of the Ying Ch'ing ware of this period has a fluency lost in the later archaisms. Contemporary with this delicate ware is, in the 13th-14th century a heavier ware, not translucent, which is known by the term 'shu-fu', 'shu office'. This was also made at Ching-te-chen and would appear to have been a high class ware designed for official use.

Yuan dynasty

With the unification of China under the invading Mongols of the Yuan dynasty and the shift of the capital back to Peking in the north, once again the northern crafts were available. A flair for decoration and bold design, and an openness to central Asian and middle eastern crafts had always been characteristics of the northerners and now they seemed to come as a fresh inspiration to the southern potters. The Kiangsi Ching-te-chen kilns started to explore the possibilities of under glaze decoration. This was already a tradition with the Tzu Chou potters using both slip and iron oxide, which gave a brown colour. Further north the Koreans had used copper and possibly cobalt. Cobalt also came to China but through the south eastern port of Chuan Chow in Fukien, and discussion arises as to the earliest use and the kilns first using cobalt. However this may be, the kilns at Ching-te-chen were the first to exploit it successfully. The early 14th century seems to be the earliest date and the potters used ground cobalt oxide in a water medium painted with a brush on to the leather hard green body. A Ying Ch'ing glaze was added and the whole once fired. The nice judgement of the quantity

Fig. 21. Stem bowl, porcelain with underglaze blue decoration, ducks and water weed within the bowl. Ching-te-chen, Kiangsi. Yuan dynasty. Ht. $6\frac{5}{8}''$ 16.74 cms. [×1386] Sayce Bequest.

and strength of cobalt to obviate rising through the glaze or running in the glaze was rapidly mastered and a long tradition of richly decorated 'blue and white' was launched (Fig. 21). The arrangement and character of the decoration appears to owe much to the northern assimilation of middle eastern ideas and this added a new flavour to Chinese ceramics. For although monochromes were always made, it was decorated porcelain which now came to the fore. After cobalt and very briefly copper under-glaze decoration had been established, the Ching-te-chen potters again accepted a decorative innovation from the north and built up a tradition of over-glaze decoration. Although this is a technique requiring two different types of firing and

28

Fig. 22. Tall necked vase, porcelain with overglaze five colour decoration. Ching-te-chen, Kiangsi. Ming, Wan-li mark. Ht. $14\frac{1}{2}''$ 37.3 cms. [×1198] Mallett Bequest.

29

must be regarded as more expensive to make, it rapidly became very popular.

Ming dynasty

First appearing in the Ming dynasty probably in the 15th century, three colours red, green and yellow, were used and are the same colours as had been used in Tzu Chou for over glaze decoration in the Sung/Chin period and in T'ang low fired wares.

The palette was expanded to five colours and used for the bold and rich decorations of a range of handsome Ming wares (Fig. 22). An Imperial office was established at Ching-te-chen within the 15th century and the influence of the taste of the court and perhaps even more of the court official became increasingly evident. At first reign marks were put on to only the wares intended for palace use, but quickly the practice extended to almost all wares. The mark is not totally reliable, it is easily applied and in later times may have been used to enhance the piece or to mislead. The Ming period was one of richness of taste and a conscious antiquarianism perhaps to mark the return to a native dynasty and a celebration of the 'old China'. Notable amongst the provincial Ming wares is the lovely white porcelain produced in Te Hua, Fukien. This porcelain clay has particular properties being much more plastic than the Ching-te-chen clay and so holding its shape during throwing or modelling and firing. The finished ware has a warm ivory glaze and a quite characteristic richness. The figurines made in the Te Hua kilns became popular in Europe and the French named the ware Blanc de Chine (pl. 23). Both over-glaze and under-glaze decoration was also produced at these kilns. The other quite different provincial Ming ware is called Fa Hua and the kiln of origin is not known. The body is of a heavy stoneware and this is decorated with a coloured palette of purple, turquoise and yellow and blue. The grand wares produced range from figurines to garden furniture (Fig. 24).

Ch'ing dynasty

The picture in the Manchu Ch'ing dynasty is technically very close, both under– and over-glaze colours were used to decorate an ever

Fig. 23. Seated lady holding a scroll and rosary. White porcelain with a translucent ivory coloured glaze. From Te Hua, Fukien. 17th century. Ht. 8″ 20.2 cms. [1956.3285] Ingram Gift.

31

Fig. 24. Large jar, heavy stoneware with slip trail decoration and Fa Hua three colour glazes, (Neck is an enamelled metal replacement). Kiln site unknown. Ming 17th century.
Ht. 14″ 35.36 cms. [×1410] Mallett Bequest.

32

Fig. 25. Plate, porcelain with underglaze blue decoration, Ching-te-chen, Kiangsi. Late 17th century. D. 11″ 27.9 cms. [1971.21].

33

Fig. 26. Tankard with silver gilt fittings, underglaze blue decoration.
Ching-te chen, Kiangsi. Mid 17th century.
Ht. 9¼" 23 cms. [1978.801] G. Reitlinger Gift.

Fig. 27. Tall vase blue and white porcelain probably from the Dehua kilns of Fujian. The dedicatory inscription gives a date of 1718 and states that this was dedicated to the Pei family Hall. Ht. 19⅘" 48.6 cms. [1986].

CHINESE CERAMICS

Fig. 28. Bowl, porcelain with Famille Rose overglaze decoration of women and children. Ching-te-chen, Kiangsi. Ch'ing dynasty. 18th century. D. 7½″ 19.05 cms. [×1412] Mallett Bequest.

36

increasing quantity of porcelain and Ching-te-chen remained the major kiln area. Stylistically the 17th century saw a movement toward elegant and dashing painterly decoration in under-glaze blue, (Fig. 25, 26, 31 and covers) a more staid decoration in polychrome and some handsome monochrome wares. The 18th century styles chime well with others of that period in other cultures. The growth of private wealth allowed of luxury, not always of the most refined. Ceramics had in many ways become de-valued in China and although porcelains of elegance and prettiness were produced in considerable quantity they no longer ranked amongst the collectors' treasures. The Famille Rose palette, adding rose pink (colloidal gold) and opaque white (arsenic) to the Famille Verte palette, lent itself to precise and decorative painting on the exquisite porcelain now possible (Fig. 28). The scholar aesthetes' taste leaned more toward archaism and a solemnity exemplified by the crackled glaze monochromes of the Ju and Kuan types (Fig. 29),

Fig. 29. Water dish in the form of a peach spray, porcelain with grey green glaze (Kuan type). Ching-te-chen, Kiangsi. Ching Yung Chang mark and period.
D. 6¼" 15.87 cms. [×1415] Sayce Bequest.

37

and the I Hsing unglazed 'basalt' wares. The court with unabashed love of the curious and exotic admired the polychrome decoration, bright monochromes and tour-de-force glazes which imitate other materials. These ceramics should take their place with other crafts to which they often formed a setting, for the well furnished Ch'ing house was full to over-flowing with objects, both useful and decorative, as the furnishing of an ever more elaborate way of living. The Peking palaces were the most exotic examples of this way of living, but there were many other very large households established in distant parts of the country. The consumption of decorative craft work of some quality was enormous and the workshops flourished. Ching-te-chen seems always to have retained its supremacy in the production of ceramics although notable kilns particularly for decoration were established in Canton and the Changsha kilns, flourishing to this day, were in production.

Fig. 30. Wine or tea-pot with silver fittings, porcelain, famille verte over glaze. Ch'ing.
Ht. 6″ 15.4 cms. [×1364] Mallett Bequest.

The ceramic industry in China today is active and demonstrates once again the change of patronage. The quality of material remains high, and traditionalism in design and decoration remain important.

Fig. 31. Large dish underglaze blue decoration. Ching-te-chen, Kiangsi. Mid to late 17th century.
D. 19″ 49 cms. [1978.2066] G. Reitlinger Gift.

Chronological Table of Chinese Periods, Dynasties and Reigns

Neolothic–Bronze Age		8th millenium–17th century BC
Shang Dynasty		17th century–1028 BC
Chou Dynasty		1028– 221 BC
Western Chou	1028– 771	
Spring and Autumn Annals	771– 481	
Warring States	481– 221	
Ch'in Dynasty		221– 206
Han Dynasty		BC 206– 221 AD
Western Han	206– 12	
Hsin	12– 23 AD	
Eastern Han	25– 221	
Western Chin Dynasty		219– 316
Eastern Chin Dynasty		317– 419
Nan Pei Ch'ao Dynasty		420– 580
Sui Dynasty		581– 618
T'ang Dynasty		618– 906
Five Dynasties		907– 960
(Liao 907–1125)		
Sung Dynasty		960–1279
Northern Sung	960–1127	
Southern Sung	1128–1279	
(Chin 1115–1234)		
Yuan Dynasty		1260–1368
Ming Dynasty		1368–1644

Hung-wu	1368–1398	Hung-chih	1488–1505
Chien wên	1399–1402	Chêng-tê	1506–1521
Yung-lo	1403–1424	Chia-ching	1522–1566
Hsüan-tê	1426–1435	Lung-ch'ing	1567–1572
Chêng-t'ung	1436–1449	Wan-li	1573–1619
Ching-t'ai	1450–1457	T'ai-ch'ang	1620
T'ien-shun	1457–1464	T'ien-ch'i	1621–1627
Ch'êng-hua	1465–1487	Ch'ung-chêng	1628–1643

Ch'ing Dynasty   1644–1911

Shun-chih	1644–1661	Tao-kuang	1821–1850
K'ang-hsi	1662–1722	Hsien-fêng	1851–1861
Yung-chêng	1723–1735	T'ung-chih	1862–1874
Ch'ien-lung	1736–1795	Kuang-hsü	1875–1908
Chia-ch'ing	1796–1820	Hsüan-t'ung	1909–1912

Republic of China	1912–1949
Peoples' Republic of China	1949–

Glossary
Romanisation of Chinese Terms

Wade/Giles	Pinyin	Wade/Giles	Pinyin
Anhwei	Anhui	Linju	Linru
Chekiang	Zhejiang	Loyang	Luoyang
Chien Yang	Jianyang	Lu Kuei-ming	Lu Guiming
Chi Chou	Jizhou	Lung Ch'uan	Longquan
Chin	Jin	Lung Ch'ing	Longqing
Chinghsien	Jingxian	Nanking	Nanjing
Ching-te-chen	Jingdezhen	Nan pei ch'ao	Nanbeichao
Chiu Yen	Jiuyan	Ningsia	Ningxia
Chou	Zhou		
Chün Chou	Junzhou	Peking	Beijing
Ch'ang an	Changan	Shansi	Shanxi
Ch'ing	Qing	Shantung	Shandong
Ch'in	Qin	Shaohsing	Saoxing
Ch'u Chou	Chuzhou	Shensi	Shaanxi
		Sian	Xian
Fukian	Fujian	Shufu	Xufu
		Sung	Song
Hangchow	Hang zhou		
Honan	Henan	Ta T'ung	Datong
Hopeh	Hebei	Tao Kuang	Daoguang
Hungchih	Hongzhi	Te Hua	Dehua
Hupeh	Hubei	Ting Chou	Ding zhou
Hsien Feng	Xianfeng	Tung Kuan	Dong guan
Hsü Yin	Xuyin	Tz'u Chou	Cizhou
Hsüan-te	Xuande	T'ai Ch'ang	Taichang
Hsüan-t'ung	Xuantong	T'ien Ch'i	Tianqi
		T'ien Mu Shan	Tianmushan
Ju	Ru	T'ien Shun	Tian Shun
		T'ungchih	Tongzhi
Kansu	Gansu		
K'anghsi	Kangxi	Wa Chia P'ing	Wajiaping
Kiangsi	Jiangxi		
Kiangsu	Jiangsu	Yi Hsing	Yixing
Kuan	Guan	Ying Ch'ing	Yingqing
Kuanghsü	Guangxu	Yueh	Yue
Kwangsi	Guangxi	Yung Cheng	Yungjeng
Kwang Tung	Guangdong		
Kweichow	Guizhou		

41

Bibliography

H. Garner: *Oriental Blue and White*, 1954. Faber and Faber
G. St. G. Gompertz: *Chinese Celadon Wares*, 1957. Faber and Faber.
D. Green: *Understanding Pottery Glazes*, 1963. Faber and Faber
M. Medley: *Yuan Porcelain and Stoneware*, 1974. Faber and Faber.
M. Medley: *The Chinese Potter*, 1977. Phaidon Press.
M. Tregear: *A Catalogue of Chinese Greenwares in the Ashmolean Museum*, 1977. Oxford University Press.
N. Wood: *Oriental Glazes*, 1978. Pitman.

Front cover: Blue underglaze decorated porcelain, Ming, Wan-Li Mark and period.
Ht. 7⅝" 19.2 cms. (X1383) Mallett Bequest.
Back cover: Detail from large dish with underglaze blue decoration.
See fig. 31. (1978. 2066).